CAMP PUZZLES

Sterling Publishing Co., Inc.
New York

2 4 6 8 10 9 7 5 3 1

Published by Sterling Publishing Co., Inc.
387 Park Avenue South, New York, NY 10016
© 2005 by Sterling Publishing Co., Inc.
This book is composed of material from the following Sterling Publishing Co., Inc. titles:
Little Giant® *Book of After School Fun* © 2000 by Sterling Publishing Co., Inc.
Classic Whodunits © 2003 by Sterling Publishing Co., Inc.

Design by StarGraphics Studio

Printed in China
All rights reserved

ISBN 1-4027-2890-5

TABLE OF CONTENTS

Optical Illusions

THE FENCE

Concentrate very hard on a point in the white field of intersecting lines for about 30 seconds. Then shift your attention quickly to one of the black squares. What do you see between the black squares?

Answer on page 62

Are the vertical lines straight? Do the crossbars go straight through them or is their pattern uneven?

Answer on page 62

MAD HAT

How does the height of this top hat (A–B) compare with the width of its brim (C–D)?

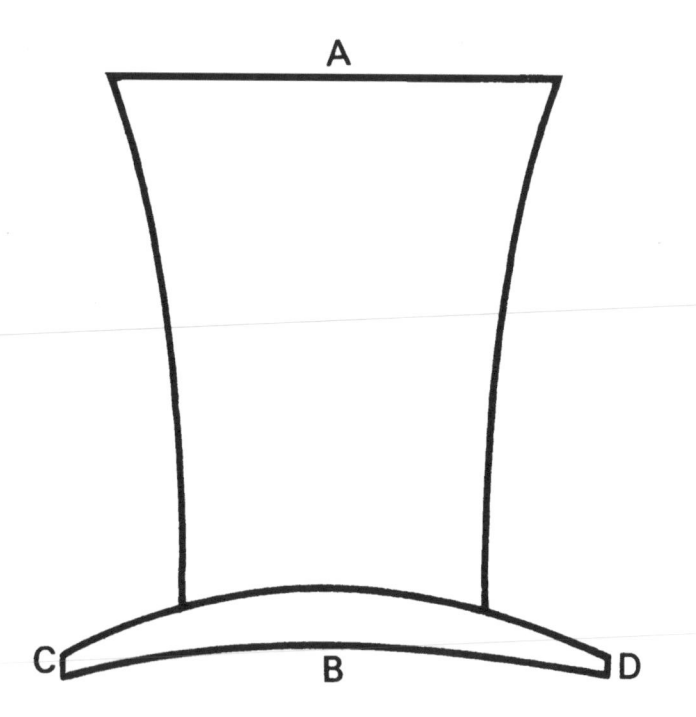

Answer on page 62

1. Is the diagonal line straight?

2. Which line is the continuation of A? B or C?

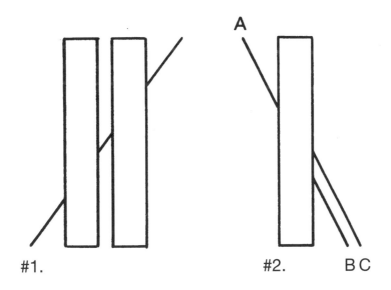

#1.　　　　　　　　　　　#2.　　　B C

Answer on page 63

THE STAIRCASE

A normal staircase? Try walking on it upside down!

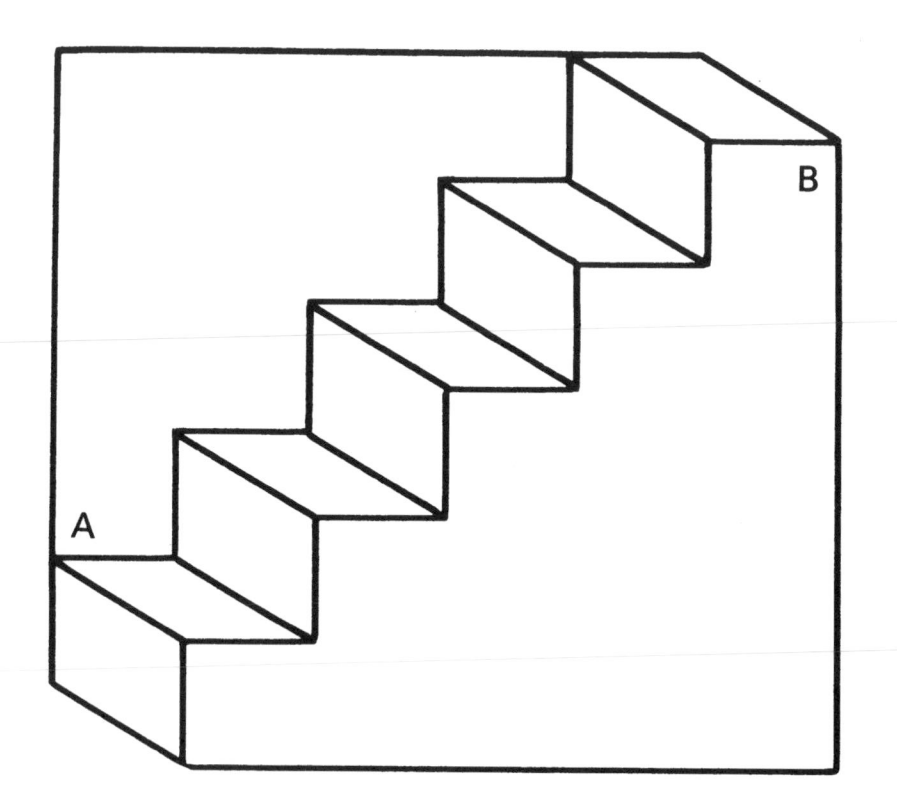

Answer on page 63

Are you looking inside a tube? Or at the top of a beach ball?

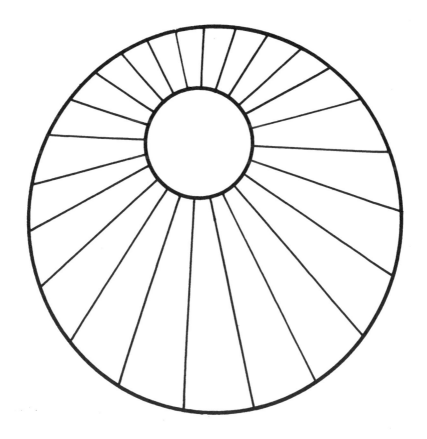

Answer on page 63

WARPED BARS

Are the white bars straight or do they bulge and bend?

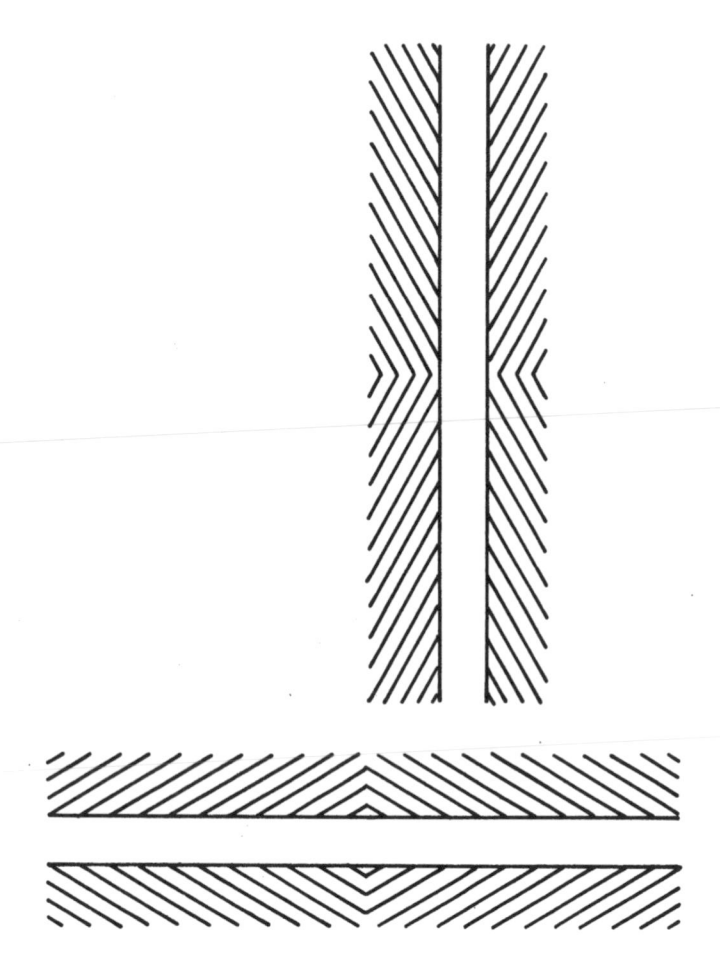

Answer on page 63

CROSSWORDS

PUZZLE #1

ACROSS

1 "Yo-ho-ho and a bottle of ____"
4 Person who makes up rhymes
8 Unit of computer memory
12 Every once ____ while (2 words)
13 "Hey, what's the big ____?"
14 There might be one on the side of a staircase
15 Game with deeds and Chance cards
17 "Excuse me . . ."
18 That girl
19 Pocket fuzz
21 Word you use during long division
24 You make soup in it
25 Sound of a ray gun
28 Rescue a car
29 Constellations are made up of them
31 Animal that gives birth to lambs
32 "____ was saying . . ." (2 words)
33 Baby goat
34 Vehicle that can handle rough terrain
35 Part of the leg
37 Sticky stuff
39 ____ Rose (famous ballplayer who was banned from baseball)
41 Game with tiles and Triple Letter Squares
46 "And they lived happily ____ after"
47 Fix mistakes in writing
48 Younger version of the word in 3-Down
49 "What ____ we thinking?"
50 Part of a camera
51 Take someone to court

DOWN

1 It surrounds a basketball net
2 Numero ____ (#1)
3 Guy
4 Frosty the Snowman had one
5 Bad smell
6 Long, skinny fish
7 Jonathan ____ Thomas
8 Ingredient in some cereals that has a lot of fiber
9 Game with dice and "small straights"
10 Make a knot
11 Kind of tree
16 Exclamation like "Aha!"
20 "____ none of your business!"

21 "Give ____ chance!" (2 words)
22 1, 2, and 3: Abbreviation
23 Game with colored circles and a spinner
24 Lily ____ (what a frog sits on)
26 In ____ of (impressed by)
27 ____ rally
29 Glide down a snowy mountain
30 Shiny stuff on a Christmas tree

34 What someone does for a living
36 In this spot
37 Smile broadly
38 Grains that horses eat
39 Long seat in church
40 Christmas ____ (December 24)
42 Letters between B and F
43 Ammo for a toy gun
44 "Skip to My ____"
45 Private ____ (detective)

Answer on page 64

PUZZLE #2

ACROSS

1 Dog, cat, or hamster, for example
4 Emergency letters
7 Jewish religious leader
12 "I ____ you one!"
13 Wolf down
14 Tim ____ ("Home Improvement" star)
15 Comic strip by Charles Schulz
17 Football team in Detroit
18 Suffix for "heir"
19 "____ sesame!"
20 Walks in water
23 Word that Scrooge said
24 When the sun is out
27 ____ rain (ecology problem)
28 Miles ____ hour
29 Drink that's made in Napa Valley
30 Kind of toothpaste
31 What groceries are put into
32 You pull them out of a garden
33 It comes at the end of a restaurant meal
35 You need it for frying

36 Birds that fly in a V-shape
38 Comic strip by Bill Amend
42 Monsters in fairy tales
43 Get older
44 "What ____ you talking about?"
45 Carries
46 ____ and reel
47 Ballpoint ____

DOWN

1 The sound a balloon makes
2 Female sheep
3 The Mad Hatter drank it
4 Dr. ____ (children's book author)
5 Some grains
6 Roads: Abbreviation
7 Character on "Happy Days"
8 Tell ____ (fib): 2 words
9 Comic strip by Chic Young
10 Big ____ (famous landmark in London)
11 Drive-____ (places where movies are watched from cars)
16 Require
19 It helps row a boat
20 What a dog's tail might do

21 "____ Ventura, Pet Detective"
22 Comic strip by Scott Adams
23 Plead
25 Hide-____-seek
26 Word of agreement
28 Good friend
29 "They ____ thataway!"
31 "____ you!" (reaction to a sneeze)
32 Polished the floor

34 "Peekaboo, ____ you!" (2 words)
35 ____ stick (bouncy toy)
36 "You've ____ to be kidding"
37 What a conceited person has a lot of
38 Distant
39 Kind of music Queen Latifah makes
40 Raw metal
41 A dozen minus a pair

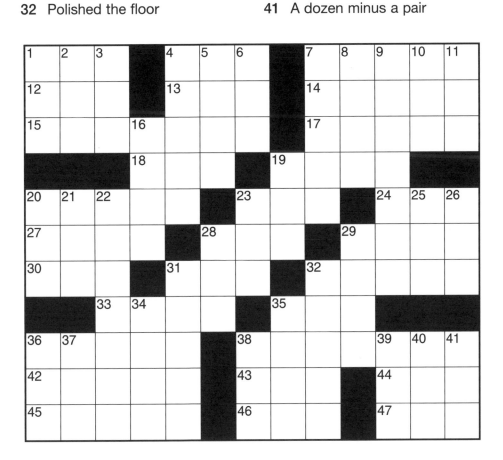

Answer on page 65

PUZZLE #3

ACROSS

1 Boxer's punches
5 Coolio's music
8 Big wooden pole on a ship
12 Words of understanding (2 words)
13 Suffix that means "most"
14 State that has a lot of Mormons
15 Disney movie
17 Not early
18 "What ____ doing here?" (2 words)
19 Health resort
21 "____ the season to be jolly . . ."
24 "Oh, what's the ____?" ("What difference does it make?")
26 Vegetable that makes you cry when you chop it
30 Stuff in a pen
31 Look without blinking
33 Number in a duo
34 Perhaps
36 Decay
37 Do what Betsy Ross was famous for doing
38 Commercials
40 Get ready to shoot a basketball
42 Not quite hot
45 Disney movie

50 Someone who lives in the Middle East
51 "____ got an idea!"
52 Final
53 Prefix for "colon" or "final"
54 Homer's neighbor on "The Simpsons"
55 Potatoes have them

DOWN

1 Brand of peanut butter
2 Red ____ beet (2 words)
3 "Boy Meets World" actor Savage
4 ____ good example (what a role model should do) (2 words)
5 "I couldn't ____" ("I just had to do it")
6 "Do ____ say!" (2 words)
7 School groups that have open houses: Abbreviation
8 Disney movie
9 One ____ time (2 words)
10 Got into a chair
11 Most commonly written word in English
16 Made other people laugh
20 Like something written in verse
21 Tiny ____ (character in "A Christmas Carol")

22 "Never ____ million years!" (2 words)
23 Where clouds are
25 Hearing organ
27 "____ been real!" ("I've had fun!")
28 Homophone of "oh"
29 At this moment
32 Sounded like a lion
35 Disney movie

39 ____ guards (protection for soccer players)
41 Stubborn animal
42 The past tense of "is"
43 "We ____ the World"
44 Male sheep
46 New Year's ____
47 Put down
48 Ending for "Japan" or "Vietnam"
49 Roads: Abbreviation

Answer on page 65

PUZZLE #4

ACROSS

1 Big crowd
4 Drink that contains caffeine
7 Raises up
12 Kwik-E-Mart worker on "The Simpsons"
13 Like the numbers 3, 11, and 19
14 Really love
15 Woman who is half fish
17 Noisy thing on a fire truck
18 ____ Frank (famous diary writer)
19 Half of twenty
21 The ____ Sea (body of water bordering Israel)
22 Celebrity
24 Short swim
26 Roads and avenues: Abbreviations
27 Command to a dog
29 ____ office (place to mail letters)
31 "Do ____ say!" (2 words)
33 Diamond or ruby, for example
35 Makes a ditch
37 Singer who used to be married to Sonny Bono

39 Money left for a waitress
41 Got bigger
43 Bees make it
45 Not in any place
47 Bert and ____ ("Sesame Street" friends)
48 Part of the foot
49 Woman in the Garden of Eden
50 People in charge of colleges
51 Pronoun for a woman
52 ____ Flanders (character on "The Simpsons")

DOWN

1 Baby's first word, sometimes
2 Unlocks
3 Crayola color (2 words)
4 "One ____ customer" (2 words)
5 Make changes in an article
6 Did sums
7 ____ Vegas, Nevada
8 "____ it!" (successful shout) (2 words)
9 Crayola color (2 words)
10 "Trick or ____!"
11 Puts in the mail

16 Hamburger or chicken, for example
20 Little bite
23 Old piece of cloth
25 It contains peas
28 So far
30 Make an "Oh well!" sound
31 Felt sore all over
32 Area next to the ocean

34 After-dinner ____ (breath-freshening candies)
36 Start a game of tennis
38 Strap that controls a horse
40 Winnie-the-____
42 Plant that you don't want in a garden
44 Word of agreement
46 Pee-____ Herman

Answer on page 66

PUZZLE #5

ACROSS

1 "The Red Planet"
5 One day ____ time (2 words)
8 Conversation
12 State where Toledo is
13 Stimpy's pal, in cartoons
14 Bart Simpson's sister
15 Bundles of paper
16 Enemy of Batman
18 "Just ____!" (Nike's slogan) (2 words)
20 Use a needle and thread
21 Good buddy
23 Small bite
25 Enter data for a computer
29 People shout it to the bullfighter
30 Scrub really hard
32 Ending for "Japan"
33 Winter coat
35 Conclusion
36 One of the Bobbsey Twins
37 "Jack ____ Jill"
39 ____ Island (part of New York)
41 Enemy of Batman (2 words, abbreviation)

45 Uncle's wife
48 Part for an actor
49 They're not yeses
50 Chest protectors for babies
51 Graceful bird
52 Letters that signal for help
53 Metal fastener

DOWN

1 Clean the floor
2 "I knew it!"
3 Enemy of Batman
4 Just okay: Hyphenated
5 Ocean near the North Pole
6 Drink that's made from leaves
7 Little bugs
8 Bozo or Ronald McDonald
9 That guy
10 White ____ sheet (2 words)
11 Slightly brown
17 Strange person
19 Crazy
21 " ____ Goes the Weasel"
22 ____ mode (with ice cream) (2 words)
24 Edgar Allan ____ (famous writer)

26 Enemy of Batman
27 Country between Canada and Mexico: Abbreviation
28 Number of arms on a squid
31 "Don't do anything ____ I tell you to"
34 Girl's name
38 Comfortable rooms in houses

40 Captures
41 Abbreviation before a wife's name
42 Move a canoe
43 Miami's state: Abbreviation
44 Place to see animals
46 Shaquille O'Neal's group: Abbreviation
47 One-thrid of a tablespoon: Abbreviation

Answer on page 66

PUZZLE #6

ACROSS

1 Sinks downward
5 Supposed ability to read minds: Abbreviation
8 Cool ____ cucumber (2 words)
11 Sign above a door, sometimes
12 Thin as a ____
14 Corny joke
15 "If it ____ up to me . . ."
16 Zoo animal
18 Planet of the ____"
20 ____ shoes (things a ballerina wears)
21 Not on
23 The square root of 100
25 They're sold by the dozen
29 TV alien from the planet Melmac
30 Stuffed-____ pizza
33 Big tree
34 Sandwich breads
36 Pekoe is a type of this
37 Baseball statistic: Abbreviation
38 Sam-____ (Dr. Seuss character): Hyphenated
41 Me, myself, ____ (2 words)
43 Zoo animal
47 Too
50 "____ and improved"
51 Captain Hook's sidekick in "Peter Pan"
52 Cole ____ (common side dish)
53 Opposite of "live"
54 Put two and two together
55 Detest

DOWN

1 Join with stitches
2 The Tin Man carried one
3 Zoo animal
4 A ____ in the right direction
5 One end of a pencil
6 ____ Francisco
7 Movie star Brad ____
8 "Many years ____ . . ."
9 It comes out of maple trees
10 Ending for "orphan" or "percent"
13 Zodiac sign that comes after Cancer
17 Grant's opponent in the Civil War
19 "And others": Abbreviation
21 Paddle for a boat
22 Go up in a plane
24 Cashew or macadamia
26 Zoo animal

27 Talk and talk and talk
28 Water-____ (have fun on a lake)
31 "Please be ____" ("Get in your chairs")
32 Light brown color
35 Take a tiny drink of
39 Sounds the doctor tells you to make
40 One of the Berenstain Bears

42 Hundred-yard ____ (kind of race)
43 "____ of the Road" (Boyz II Men song)
44 Ring of flowers they give out in Hawaii
45 She gives birth to a lamb
46 Boy's name
48 Weekend day: Abbreviation
49 "I ____ you one!" ("I'm in your debt!")

Answer on page 67

PUZZLE #7

ACROSS

1 It forms on top of a wound
5 Janitors use them
9 Tiny ____ ("A Christmas Carol" character)
12 Part of a golf course
13 Tell ____ (don't tell the truth) (2 words)
14 Astonishment
15 Ending for "respect"
16 Place, like on the Internet
17 Amount at an auction
18 Ice cream flavor (2 words)
21 Shade of brown
22 It lives in a hive
23 Room in a prison
24 Ending for "count" or "baron"
25 "Mighty ____ Young" (movie about a gorilla)
27 Separate with a sieve
30 2,000 pounds
31 Music recordings, for short
34 Ice cream flavor (2 words)
38 X-____ vision (one of Superman's powers)
39 Direction on a compass
40 Green citrus fruit
41 Munched on
42 Not early
43 Last word of a prayer
44 What the P stands for in "MPH"
45 Moved quickly
46 Annoying person

DOWN

1 The long, thin part of an arrow
2 Snake that has a hood
3 Woody ____ (famous movie director)
4 "Where have you ____?"
5 Makes potatoes ready for eating
6 ____ Oyl (Popeye's girlfriend)
7 Bread that has a pocket
8 Looked at
9 Kitchen furniture
10 "____ Always Love You" (Whitney Houston song) (2 words)
11 What an Olympic winner gets
19 One of the TV networks
20 Cubes that are in the freezer
24 "And on and on": Abbreviation

25 Wrote down in a hurry
26 Half of two
27 ____ heap (pile of junk)
28 " ____ you!" ("You're not my friend anymore!") (2 words)
29 Area near the front door, in some houses
30 Try the food

31 Wind ____ (thing that hangs outside and makes jingly sounds)
32 Ten-cent coins
33 Used cash
35 Nighttime birds with big eyes
36 Jump
37 Applaud

Answer on page 67

PUZZLE #8

ACROSS
1 "Get ____ my back!"
4 Joint near the middle of the body
7 Command a dog learns in obedience school
11 ____ Blanc (person who did the voice of Bugs Bunny)
12 They go on kings or twos in the card game Spit
14 State where Cincinnati is
15 "Prince ____" (song in the movie "Aladdin")
16 You go camping in one
17 Person who's not cool
18 Presses on a horn
20 "I'm ____ kidding!"
22 The Mediterranean ____
23 Prefix for "gravity" or "freeze"
24 Big structure in Egypt
26 Five-pointed thing
28 Important test
29 Home music systems
31 Health resorts
34 "____ says so?"
35 It's used to make roads
36 Copy of a magazine
37 ____ and rave (argue loudly)
39 Word that appears on the thing at 6-down
41 Kind of poem (homophone for "owed")
42 Like the numbers 2, 4, and 6
43 Tools for gardeners
44 Tiny nibble
45 What a bird builds
46 Place for a pig
47 "Help us!"

DOWN
1 Big city in Nebraska
2 Criminal
3 Cartoon set in caveman times, with "The"
4 Head coverings
5 Put frosting on a cake
6 Small coin
7 Father's boy
8 Cartoon set in Springfield (2 words)
9 Showed on television, for example
10 Wise creature in the "Star Wars" films
13 Shopping places
19 "Go fly a ____!"
21 What the Internal Revenue Service collects
24 "Practice what you ____!"

25 Boston's state:
   Abbreviation
27 Paintings and so on
29 Get rid of a beard
30 Cookies with white
   middles
32 Word that can go
   before "visual"
33 Oozes

34 Small brown bird
36 "The ____-Bitsy
   Spider"
38 Stuff that can
   cause an explosion:
   Abbreviation
40 A fisherman might
   throw it into the
   water

Answer on page 68

CROSSWORDS

PUZZLE #9

ACROSS

1 What keys fit into
6 " ____ my pleasure"
9 Get at a store
12 Musical that includes the song "Tomorrow"
13 "How ____ you?"
14 Sly ____ fox (2 words)
15 Kriss Kringle's other name
16 Mother
17 Uncle ____ (symbol of America
18 Word that might end a list: Abbreviation
20 Little ____ Muffet
22 Work in the movies
25 Big chunk of something
27 "I made a mistake!"
30 ____ of (in a way)
32 A while ____ (in the past)
33 Someone who isn't interesting
34 What the "big hand" points to
35 Some people pay it every month
37 "Do ____ Pass Go . . ." (phrase in the game Monopoly)
38 It can go before "skirt" or "van"
40 You might get it pierced
42 ____ code (number at the end of an address)
44 Now ____ then
46 The end of one of Aesop's Fables
50 Card with just one symbol on it
51 Split ____ soup
52 Run away to get married
53 " ____ out of here!"
54 Messy place
55 Did some stitching

DOWN

1 ____ Vegas
2 "I'm ____ roll!" (2 words)
3 TV channel that shows mostly news
4 Toy that has a long tail
5 Chairs
6 "Do you know who ____ ?" (2 words)
7 Orchestra instrument
8 Prefix for "finals" or "annual"
9 Orchestra instrument
10 Country formed in 1776: Abbreviation
11 Vegetable also called a sweet potato

19 Orchestra instrument
21 Weep loudly
22 What's left after something is burned
23 Sound a pigeon makes
24 Orchestra instrument
26 Number of years you've been around
28 ____ wrestling (Hulk Hogan's sport)
29 All ____ (ready to go)
31 Beginning for "cycle"
36 Makes less wild
39 Takes a short sleep
41 Part in a play
42 Zig and ____
43 Skating surface
45 24 hours
47 Pull on the oars
48 Monkey's big relative
49 Didn't follow

Answer on page 68

CROSSWORDS

WORD SEARCH

THE SIMPSONS

```
D  L  E  I  F  G  N  I  R  P  S
T  O  D  H  E  O  S  P  A  A  R
Y  E  N  R  A  B  B  C  P  E  E
B  A  A  U  L  I  E  M  N  S  N
W  A  K  H  T  O  A  S  I  E  N
H  M  R  B  U  R  N  S  D  J  I
Y  O  A  T  G  W  U  F  N  P  K
H  O  B  N  O  M  L  C  E  C  S
C  A  A  S  K  A  I  I  L  A  R
T  O  P  N  N  R  G  A  S  R  U
A  R  P  D  E  G  U  I  O  K  O
R  A  E  N  A  E  L  S  N  T  M
C  R  L  M  G  Y  H  C  T  I  Y
S  A  N  D  O  K  O  O  D  Y  E
O  S  S  R  E  H  T  I  M  S  S
```

BARNEY	ITCHY	NED FLANDERS
BART	JIMBO	NELSON
DONUT	KRUSTY	OTTO
EDNA KRABAPPEL	LISA	SCRATCHY
GRAMPA	MAGGIE	SEYMOUR SKINNER
HOMER	MARGE	SMITHERS
	MR. BURNS	SPRINGFIELD

Answer on page 69

CIRCLING THE BASES

```
            B  T  C
         A  E  H  E  A
      S  T  R  I  K  E  T
   E  E  Y  I  E  V  R  U  C
H  O  I  U  P  N  R  E  M  O  H
I  G  E  R  S  M  T  M  T  A  C  J  E
T  T  R  O  E  P  U  R  E  T  T  A  B  K  R
P  N  R  E  S  O  U  T  F  I  E  L  D  L  B
L  U  O  N  D  E  C  K  P  H  E  A  G  A  U
B  E  E  L  I  R  D  F  O  U  L  C  B
   W  K  R  A  L  S  E  N  A  K  G
      E  O  I  F  S  R  I  S  F
      W  H  T  E  R  T  E
         H  C  A  O  C
            N  P  R
```

BACKSTOP	COACH	OUTFIELD
BALK	CURVE	SLIDER
BASE HIT	ERROR	STRIKE
"BATTER UP!"	FOUL	UMPIRE
BUNT	HOMER	WILD PITCH
CATCHER	NO-HITTER	WORLD SERIES
CHOKE UP	ON DECK	

Answer on page 70

MONOPOLY GAME

```
E  T  N  E  R  M  Y  P  O  N  B
O  S  K  R  O  W  R  E  T  A  W
S  E  U  P  O  O  L  Y  N  P  R
O  H  P  O  P  E  R  K  T  O  I
E  C  O  E  H  N  E  K  O  T  M
S  Y  R  R  O  R  A  R  E  N  K
L  T  X  A  T  Y  R  U  X  U  L
Y  I  A  M  E  L  A  E  D  D  A
A  N  A  F  L  T  I  E  I  R  W
S  U  T  J  R  C  L  N  C  E  D
E  M  T  S  H  I  R  N  E  A  R
R  M  T  A  L  A  O  M  N  T  A
D  O  N  O  T  P  A  S  S  G  O
I  C  L  C  C  G  D  I  T  Y  B
E  C  A  L  P  K  R  A  P  N  J
```

BANKER	GAME	PROPERTY
BOARDWALK	HOTEL	RAILROAD
CHANCE	HOUSE	RENT
COMMUNITY CHEST	JAIL	ROLL
DICE	LUXURY TAX	SHORT LINE
DO NOT PASS GO	MONEY	TOKEN
	PARK PLACE	WATER WORKS

Answer on page 71

WORD SEARCH

PIECE A PIZZA

```
N O O O M A E F T
T T A N C H O V I E S
T E L A R A H O I W I T Y
O S U G A S L M I L N C E A
B U E M U S H R O O M I
R R T R Y E O U R R
O C L H E G A E
C I L R A G P
C V A E T P R O
O O B A E L D U M I
L S T P T A T H B I S P
I W A A A N P A R M E S A N
S E U M T S A U S A G E E
M A C O S Y T A S H P
I E E T O N I O N
```

ANCHOVIES	MEATBALL	PESTO
BROCCOLI	MUSHROOM	ROMANO
CRUST	OLIVE	SALT
EGGPLANT	ONION	SAUCE
FETA	OREGANO	SAUSAGE
GARLIC	PARMESAN	TOMATO
HAMBURGER	PEPPERONI	

Answer on page 72

```
E  C  A  R  D  E  G  G  E  L  3
T  H  2  E  E  E  3  2  S  P  2
3  D  5  O  T  9  I  T  E  O  1
2  W  O  H  G  F  4  A  B  E  S
S  S  A  S  B  C  T  S  A  A  A
E  L  L  Y  E  D  E  9  B  1  Y
S  1  S  M  B  V  4  E  Y  E  S
S  E  T  E  I  U  C  O  L  B  A
A  U  Y  L  1  A  L  W  O  A  E
L  Y  9  K  T  T  I  B  N  C  C
G  4  H  C  L  U  B  K  5  O  E
D  T  H  U  2  S  O  1  L  N  A
3  2  1  B  L  A  S  T  O  F  F
2  B  Y  2  O  E  4  I  N  N  G
7  4  4  1  7  5  E  K  A  T  1
```

BABYLON 5	9 LIVES	3-D GLASSES
CATCH-22	9 TO 5	3-LEGGED RACE
COLT .45	1-ON-1	3-PEAT
EASY AS 1, 2, 3	1, 2, BUCKLE MY SHOE	3-2-1 BLASTOFF!
49ER	R2-D2	3-WAY BULB
4-EYES	TAKE 5	2-BY-4
4-H CLUB		2 IF BY SEA

Answer on page 73

MODERN ELECTRONICS

```
H C T A W S C H V O X
W M V R T A R A T O S
N Y C E E E I T B E A
E M R S T M H M E L T
N E S N E C O R W E E
O O I D A O I T R D L
H R I Y B M O D E M L
P O U T R P K P N P I
L A A R A U A L N E T
L N G T S T H A A V E
E E A E O E S T C W D
C Y O E R R U Y S R I
O I D A R M F M A A S
N I N T E N D O G L H
V O I C E M A I L E P
```

AM-FM RADIO	PAGER	SWATCH
BOOMBOX	PLAYSTATION	VCRS
CABLE	PRINTER	VIDEOTAPE
CELL PHONE	REMOTE	VOICE MAIL
COMPUTER	SATELLITE DISH	WALKMAN
MODEM	SCANNER	WEB TV
NINTENDO	STEREO	

Answer on page 74

```
K N O C K O N W O O D
C F L L A B T H G I E
A I N D E M S I C S N
R T H I R T E E N U G
C A C A B K H E V P N
A A H D G S A U P E P
N C A E I N N E M R N
O Y N W B I S O R S T
P H C J I N X R O T U
E O E C G S A H T I S
T T G O U I H L B T R
S I N N R O B G I G
R A B B I T S F O O T
O O O D T B L E U N C
K W H O R S E S H O E
```

BIG BREAK	EIGHT BALL	RAINBOW
BINGO	HORSESHOE	SEVEN
CHANCE	JINX	STEP ON A CRACK
CHARM	KNOCK ON WOOD	STREAK
CURSE	LOTTO	SUPERSTITION
DICE	OMEN	THIRTEEN
	RABBIT'S FOOT	WISHBONE

Answer on page 75

"OH, HORRORS"

```
D  R  O  T  A  N  I  M  R  E  T
M  E  O  R  I  E  L  U  O  H  G
H  O  M  L  S  R  R  M  O  R  M
O  V  B  O  G  E  Y  M  A  N  M
I  O  O  E  N  S  K  Y  H  I  O
G  O  D  Z  I  L  L  A  A  E  N
V  E  Y  H  A  D  L  C  N  T  S
M  O  S  U  S  N  T  I  T  S  T
E  D  N  R  N  A  S  C  V  N  E
G  R  A  V  E  R  O  B  B  E  R
A  H  T  U  I  R  H  L  A  K  D
L  T  C  H  L  A  G  N  A  N  N
O  Y  H  T  A  O  T  O  E  A  H
N  E  E  R  I  H  T  I  A  R  W
M  O  R  N  S  W  F  T  E  F  R
```

ALIENS	GHOST	MUMMY
BODY SNATCHER	GHOUL	OGRE
BOGEYMAN	GOBLIN	SNAKES
DEMON	GODZILLA	TERMINATOR
DEVIL	GRAVE ROBBER	WITCH
FIEND	MEGALON	WRAITH
FRANKENSTEIN	MONSTER	

Answer on page 76

FAMOUS LAST WORDS

```
B  R  T  I  L  L  S  C  N  T  A
R  E  V  L  I  S  O  Y  I  H  E
X  G  G  A  T  T  I  I  O  A  C
M  N  T  O  B  E  D  L  S  T  O
A  A  A  Y  O  U  A  O  N  S  M
T  R  A  R  S  D  G  A  I  A  E
M  T  R  C  O  S  H  O  O  L  B
F  S  R  I  U  A  T  O  F  L  A
T  A  A  H  V  Y  O  L  E  F  C
M  E  R  A  C  E  K  A  T  O  K
R  B  E  E  L  E  D  T  H  L  A
S  T  T  D  W  S  A  E  L  K  A
V  N  O  I  S  E  T  R  R  S  A
U  O  Y  E  V  O  L  I  B  C  A
T  D  B  Y  G  N  O  L  O  S  I
```

"ADIOS"	"DON'T BE A STRANGER"	"SEE YA"
"ALOHA"	"FAREWELL"	"SHOO!"
"ARRIVEDERCI"	"HI-YO, SILVER!"	"SO LONG"
"BE GOOD"	"I LOVE YOU"	"TAKE CARE"
"BUG OFF!"	"LATER"	"TA-TA"
"CIAO"	"SCRAM!"	"THAT'S ALL, FOLKS!"
"COME BACK!"		"TOODLE-OO!"

Answer on page 77

WHODUNITS

Sherlock Holmes and Dr. Watson were relaxing by the fire in the study of 221b Baker Street. Holmes was puffing on his favorite pipe while Watson was reading the Times. Suddenly, Watson glanced over the top of the newspaper and looked directly at Holmes. "When is your birthday, Holmes?" he asked.

"You tell me, Watson," Holmes replied with a smile. "The day before yesterday I was thirty-two, and next year I will be thirty-five!"

"Impossible!" snapped Watson.

But Holmes was right. Can you tell on what day of the year Holmes celebrated his birthday?

Answer on page 78

WISHING WELL

While working on a case Dr. Watson accidentally fell down a 30–foot dry wishing well. Sherlock Holmes lowered him down a rope.

"Can you climb up?" shouted Holmes. "I'll be out before you know it!" came Watson's reply.

But the climb wasn't as easy as Watson had first imagined. Each hour he managed to climb 3 feet—but slipped back 2 feet.

How long did it take Watson to get out?

Answer on page 78

ORDER OF FINISH

Holmes and Watson decided to have a quiet day at the races. They arrived in time to catch the first race. The race was between five horses: MANOR PARK, PEANUTS, ROYAL MILE, DUSKY, and EASTERN CLASSIC.

MANOR PARK finished in front of PEANUTS, but behind ROYAL MILE. DUSKY finished in front of EASTERN CLASSIC, but behind PEANUTS.

In which order did they finish the race?

Answer on page 78

THREE THIEVES

Sherlock Holmes apprehended three thieves: Robert, Walter, and Frank. Each of them had robbed a house in a different part of London at approximately the same time. Robert, who was the oldest, didn't commit his crime in Ealing, and Walter didn't rob the house in Clapham. The one who robbed the house in Ealing didn't steal the gold watch. The one who robbed the house in Clapham stole the landscape painting. Walter didn't steal the silver coins.

In what part of London did Frank commit his crime, and what did he steal?

Answer on page 78

Holmes received a hand-delivered note that he studied for a short time before passing it to Watson.

"It's some sort of code!" exclaimed Watson. "What does it mean and who is it from?"

Holmes grabbed his hat and coat. "It's from Moriarty, Watson. Hurry, we must stop him!"

The message read:

J XJMM SPC UIF CBOL PG
FOHMBOE UPOJHIU.
NPSJBSUZ.

Holmes had obviously deciphered the message. Can you?

Answer on page 78

SNOOKER

Holmes and Watson were playing pool in their club when they were joined by Inspector Lestrade and his sergeant. Someone suggested that they have a competition using only the fifteen red balls. For each red ball sunk, the player would receive one point. The four of them would play each other once. Each game would end when all the red balls had been sunk. The winner of the competition would be the player who scored the most points.

1. Holmes scored twice as many points as Watson in their game.
2. Only one point separated Holmes and Lestrade in their game.
3. Watson beat the sergeant by five points.
4. The sergeant scored one less point against Holmes than he did against Watson.
5. Watson sank seven balls more than Lestrade.
6. Holmes finished with an odd number of points.
7. The sergeant finished with eighteen points.

Who won the competition and how many points did each player score?

Answer on page 78

COUNTRY DINNER

General Smithers invited five people to his country house for dinner. The surnames of the guests were: Forest, Giles, Handy, Jackson and King. Their vocations were: doctor, actress,

lawyer, banker and writer (but not necessarily in that order). During the meal Smithers dropped dead from food poisoning. The poison had been slipped into his meal by one of the guests. When Sherlock Holmes arrived on the scene, he was given the following information:

1. Jackson arrived last, the doctor arriving just ahead of her.
2. The writer and the actress arrived before Giles.
3. Third to arrive was the lawyer, just ahead of King.
4. Forest had seen the actress put the poison on Smither's plate.

Holmes took the actress to Scotland Yard for further questioning. Who was the actress?

Answer on page 79

THE SAFETY DEPOSIT BOX

While working on a case, Holmes received vital information from a mysterious source in the form of a note.

The note read:

"Go to the Dunwick Bank. Inside each of the safety deposit boxes listed below you will find a clue to the crime you are presently investigating.

"BOX NUMBERS: 20, 80, 76, 19, 23, 92, 88, and ?

"I have omitted to tell you the number of the last box, but I'm sure a great detective such as yourself will know where to look."

Holmes read the note and then passed it to Dr. Watson.

"Most inconvenient," muttered Watson. "Now we'll have to open every single safety deposit box to find the clue."

"Not so, Watson," replied Holmes. "I know exactly which box to open. Come along, let's hurry to the Dunwick Bank."

What was the number of the last safety deposit box?

Answer on page 79

"I've just received a note from Moriarty," Holmes informed Dr. Watson. "He intends to rob a house on Baker Street this evening."

"Great Scott! Which house, Holmes?" inquired Watson.

"That's just it, Watson. He doesn't say, but he has given us several clues."

From the clues listed below, can you work out the number of the house Moriarty intends to rob?

1. The last digit is twice the first digit.
2. The sum of the first digit and the last digit is equal to the second digit.
3. The sum of all three digits is twice that of the second digit.
4. The first digit is an even number.

Answer on page 79

VICTIM MEETING

Eight men, all of whom had recently been robbed by Professor Moriarty, met in a conference room of a fashionable London Hotel. Sherlock Holmes had received an invitation to attend the meeting. When Holmes arrived he found the eight men sitting at a table (see diagram). From the following information can you identify the position of each man at the table and his vocation?

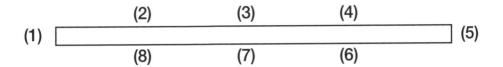

1. The vet and the dentist sat opposite each other.
2. The chairman of the meeting sat in position one, with Adams to his left.
3. Wilson sat in an even-numbered position with the banker to his left.
4. The doctor had the solicitor to his right.
5. Clark, not Brown, sat in position three, directly opposite the butcher.
6. The baker sat in position five, with Jones to his left and Dawson to his right.
7. Smith sat to the left of the vet.
8. Black, who sat opposite Clark, had the surgeon on his left.

Answer on page 79

WHODUNITS

SYNCHRONIZE YOUR WATCHES!

Holmes and Watson had set their pocket watches to the same time. Unknown to them, Watson's watch was running exactly two minutes per hour slow, and the watch belonging to Holmes was going exactly a minute per hour too fast. Later, when they checked their watches again, it was discovered that the watch belonging to Holmes was exactly one hour ahead of Watson's watch.

How long had it been since they had originally set their watches?

Answer on page 79

WHO'S WHO AT THE TABLE?

Holmes had been introduced to four musicians: two men, Frank and Harold, and two women, Ethel and Georgina.

One played the french horn, another the cymbals, the third was a trumpeter and the fourth, like Holmes, a violinist. All four were seated at a square table.

From the clues listed below, can you identify the musician who played the same instrument as Holmes?

1. The person who sat across from Frank played the french horn.
2. The person who sat across from Harold was not the trumpeter.
3. The person who sat on Ethel's left played the cymbals.
4. The person on Georgina's left was not the violinist.
5. The trumpeter and the violinist were brother and sister.

Answer on page 79

THE CASE OF THE HARD-BOILED EGG

As part of his own specially devised diet, Dr. Watson needed to eat, every day, an egg that had been boiled for 15 minutes. On the first day he asked Mrs. Hudson to prepare the egg for him.

"I only have a 7-minute hourglass and an 11-minute hourglass," complained Mrs. Hudson. "So it can't be done."

"Of course it can," interrupted Holmes, and he proceeded to show Mrs. Hudson how.

Can you find the QUICKEST way to time the boiling of the egg?

Answer on page 80

LIBRARY BOOKS

Holmes, Watson, Lestrade, Moriarty, and Mrs. Hudson all belonged to the same library. All five were returning books at the same time. The library shelved its books in alphabetical order by title instead of author.

Borrower	Title
Holmes	GREAT DETECTIVES
Watson	MEDICINE
Hudson	THE COOK BOOK
Moriarty	GREAT CRIMINALS
Lestrade	POLICE

1. None of the borrowers returned the book listed against their name above.
2. Two books were overdue. Watson had one, and the other was "MEDICINE."
3. The books returned by Holmes and Watson sat next to each other on the shelf.
4. Mrs. Hudson had to pay a fine for a late return.

Can you match up all five titles with the borrowers?

Answer on page 80

ONE MEASLY DIAMOND

Moriarty and his two partners in crime, Fingers and Porky, sat looking at the diamonds piled on the table in front of them. There was a knock at the door, which Porky answered. Mr. X, the brains behind the robbery, entered. Moriarty sent Porky to check the surrounding area to make sure that Mr. X had not been followed.

Mr. X then took Porky's seat at the table. They sat in silence for several moments, until Moriarty bent forward and took half the diamonds plus one from the pile. Mr. X then took two-thirds of what remained, placed them in his pocket and, without a word, left the building. Fingers then took two-thirds of what remained and placed them in a bag. He smiled at Moriarty and took one more diamond, which he quickly shoved into the top pocket of his coat.

When Porky returned, he glanced down at the solitary diamond lying on the table.

"Is this all I get, one measly diamond?" he grunted.

How many diamonds had originally been on the table?

Answer on page 80

DINNER AT LADY MCBRIDE'S

Dr. Watson, who had been keeping an eye on events at Lady McBride's dinner party, reported back to Sherlock Holmes at 221b Baker Street.

"I need to know the arrival times of the guests, Watson," said Holmes.

Watson glanced at his notepad. "Yes, here it is. The arrival times are as follows," said Watson. "7:30, 7:45, 7:50, 7:59, 8:05, with the last guest arriving at 8:20."

"Very good, Watson," said Holmes. "But I need to know just exactly which guest arrived at which time."

"Oh," said Watson, somewhat embarrassed. "I didn't write that down, Holmes." Eventually Watson was able to pass the following information to Holmes:

1. Lady Barclay, who wasn't the first to arrive, arrived before Lord Hadden.
2. Sir Harry Trump arrived 15 minutes after Lord Winterbottom.
3. It was one of the ladies who arrived 6 minutes after Sir John Penn.
4. Lady James arrived 15 minutes before Lord Hadden.

Can you deduce the exact arrival time of each of the six guests?

Answer on page 80

STAKE OUT THE PROFESSOR

Sherlock Holmes sat by the fire at 221b Baker Street, studying some information on a note.

"What's that you're reading, Holmes?" asked Watson.

"It's a list of houses on Fitzroy Street that have all been robbed in the last six days by Professor Moriarty."

Watson glanced at the list, which read:

MONDAY	NO. 4
TUESDAY	NO. 16
WEDNESDAY	NO. 12
THURSDAY	NO. 3
FRIDAY	NO. 7
SATURDAY	NO. 28

"Great Scott!" exclaimed Watson. "And today's Sunday. He'll probably strike again tonight."

"He will, Watson," replied Holmes. "But this time we'll be waiting inside the house for him."

Which house on Fitzroy Street will Moriarty rob next?

Answer on page 80

OPTICAL ILLUSIONS

THE FENCE

Inside the black squares, you see an even blacker lattice design! Why?

After you concentrate on a picture for a while, your eyes get tired. The most tired parts are certain spots on the "retina," the part of the eye which contains light-sensitive cells.The brightest tones cause the greatest stress to these cells, which gradually become less sensitive to light. When you look away from the white lines, the nerve endings that are less tired lightly reproduce the darker sections of the picture. Your eye transforms a negative into a positive. Here you have become tired of seeing the white lines.Your eyes record the black instead, when you shift your attention.

NIGHTMARE FOREST

They are straight. Tilt the book all the way back and you'll have proof!

MAD HAT

They are the same. Usually we overestimate vertical distance, whether it's the distance from a house roof to a plane or just the drawing on the page.

UNSURE LINES

1. Yes, but when you break a straight line with a solid bar, the straight line seems displaced.
2. "B" is the continuation of "A." "C" looks as though it connects with "A" because the solid bar "displaces" the line.

THE STAIRCASE

Depending on how you focus on the letters, the staircase can run up from A to B or you could be standing beneath the upside-down version. To see it upside down, focus on the A.

LOOKING AROUND

Either one.

WARPED BARS

They are perfectly straight.

CROSSWORDS

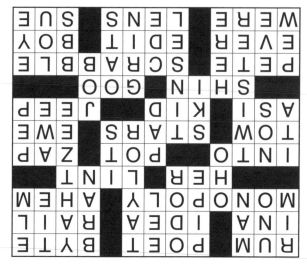

PUZZLE #1

PUZZLE #2

PUZZLE #3

PUZZLE #4

M	O	B	■	T	E	A	■	L	I	F	T	S
A	P	U	■	O	D	D	■	A	D	O	R	E
M	E	R	M	A	I	D	■	S	I	R	E	N
A	N	N	E	■	T	E	N	■	D	E	A	D
■	S	T	A	R	■	D	I	P	■	S	T	S
■	■	S	T	A	Y	■	P	O	S	T	■	■
A	S	I	■	G	E	M	■	D	I	G	S	■
C	H	E	R	■	T	I	P	■	G	R	E	W
H	O	N	E	Y	■	N	O	W	H	E	R	E
E	R	N	I	E	■	T	O	E	■	E	V	E
D	E	A	N	S	■	S	H	E	■	N	E	D

PUZZLE #5

M	A	R	S	■	A	T	A	■	C	H	A	T
O	H	I	O	■	R	E	N	■	L	I	S	A
P	A	D	S	■	C	A	T	W	O	M	A	N
■	■	D	O	I	T	■	S	E	W	■	■	■
P	A	L	■	N	I	P	■	I	N	P	U	T
O	L	E	■	S	C	O	U	R	■	E	S	E
P	A	R	K	A	■	E	N	D	■	N	A	N
■	■	■	A	N	D	■	L	O	N	G	■	■
M	R	F	R	E	E	Z	E	■	A	U	N	T
R	O	L	E	■	N	O	S	■	B	I	B	S
S	W	A	N	■	S	O	S	■	S	N	A	P

PUZZLE #6

PUZZLE #7

PUZZLE #8

O	F	F		H	I	P		S	T	A	Y
M	E	L		A	C	E	S		O	H	I	O
A	L	I		T	E	N	T		N	E	R	D
H	O	N	K	S		N	O	T		S	E	A
A	N	T	I		P	Y	R	A	M	I	D	
	S	T	A	R		E	X	A	M		
	S	T	E	R	E	O	S		S	P	A	S
W	H	O		T	A	R		I	S	S	U	E
R	A	N	T		C	E	N	T		O	D	E
E	V	E	N		H	O	E	S		N	I	P
N	E	S	T		S	T	Y		S	O	S

PUZZLE #9

L	O	C	K	S		I	T	S		B	U	Y
A	N	N	I	E		A	R	E		A	S	A
S	A	N	T	A		M	O	M		S	A	M
	E	T	C		M	I	S	S		
A	C	T		S	L	A	B		O	O	P	S
S	O	R	T		A	G	O		B	O	R	E
H	O	U	R		R	E	N	T		N	O	T
	M	I	N	I		E	A	R		
Z	I	P		A	N	D		M	O	R	A	L
A	C	E		P	E	A		E	L	O	P	E
G	E	T		S	T	Y		S	E	W	E	D

THE SIMPSONS

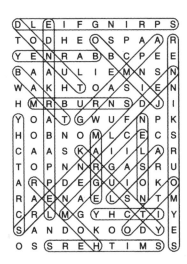

CIRCLING THE BASES

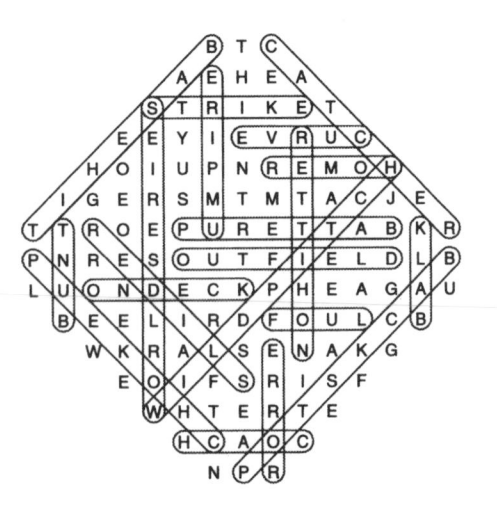

MONOPOLY GAME

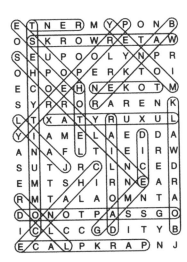

PIECE A PIZZA

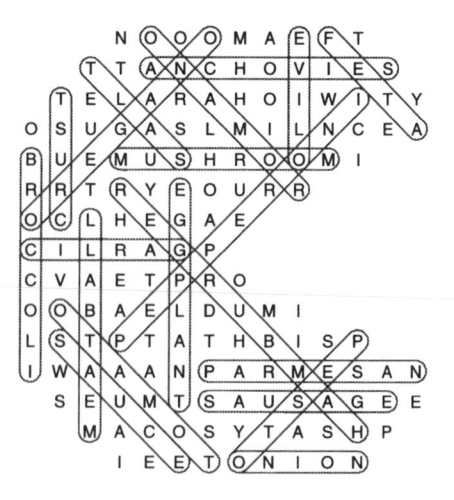

BY THE NUMBERS

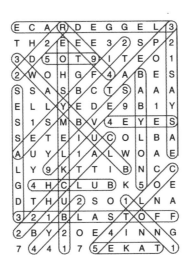

MODERN ELECTRONICS

FEELING LUCKY?

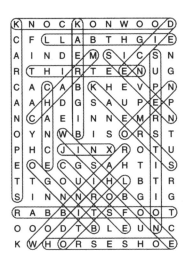

"OH, HORRORS!"

FAMOUS LAST WORDS

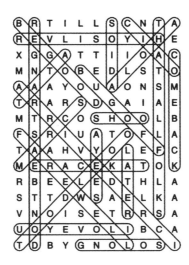

WHODUNITS

HAPPY BIRTHDAY, DEAR SHERLOCK
December 31.

WISHING WELL
28 hours.

ORDER OF FINISH
1st Royal Mile
2nd Manor Park
3rd Peanuts
4th Dusky
and finally, Eastern Classic

THREE THIEVES
Ealing and the silver coins.

MESSAGE FROM MORIARTY
Each letter in the code represents the letter that it follows in the alphabet. Therefore, the code reads: "I will rob the Bank of England tonight. Moriarty."

SNOOKER
Holmes with 29 points, followed by Watson with 26 points, Lestrade with 17 points, and the sergeant with 18 points.